3

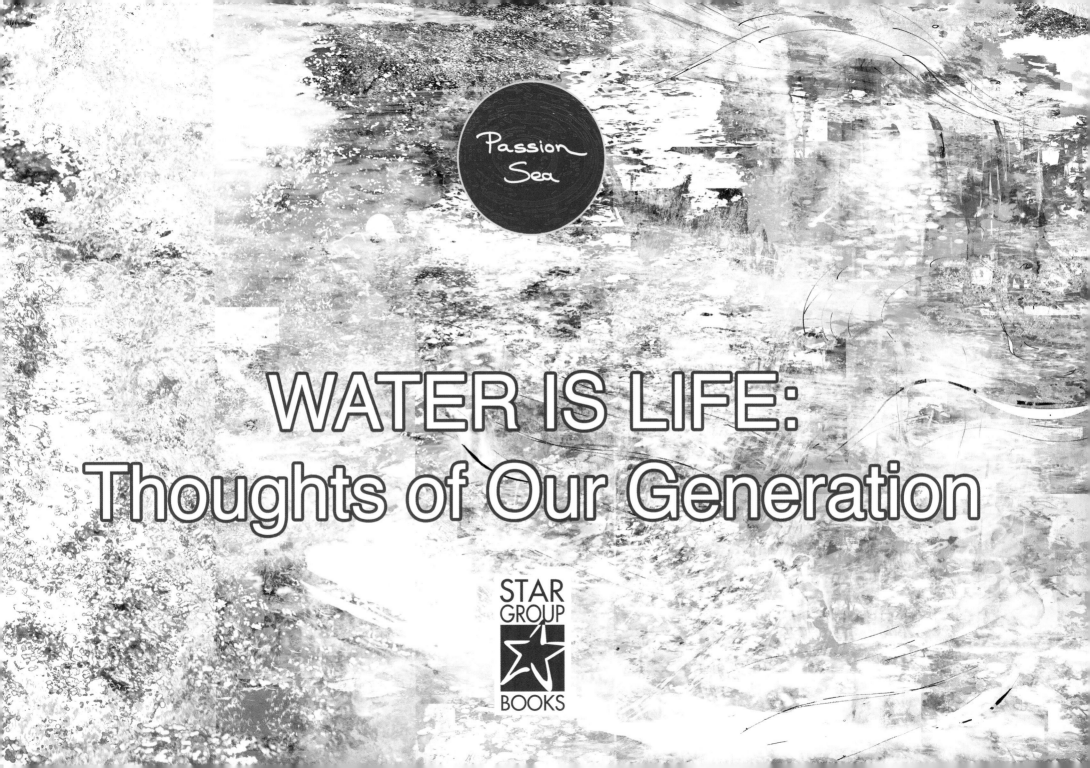

Passion
Sea

WATER IS LIFE:
Thoughts of Our Generation

STAR
GROUP
BOOKS

Published by StarGroup Books
www.stargroupinternational.com

Creative direction, concept development, cover annd interior design, original artwork, illustrations & education content: Fiona Life

Ambassador & CEO: Helga Piaget

Editor & strategic advisor: Lexye Aversa

Other education content: Professor Alessandro Leto

Other contributors: Sonja Vidovic and Miran Vamberger

Printed in Canada.
Library of Congress: 2017959580
Water is Life: Thoughts of Our Generation
ISBN: 978-1- 884886-44- 7

Acknowledgements

Passion Sea wants to thank everyone who was involved in this project. Your passion and support have filled our heart and we want to spread it into the world.

This book is dedicated to the children... their hopes, dreams and education. May this book inspire them. May their their love and gratitude for Water deepen. Finally may their knowledge and vision widen.

Special thanks to the art contest jury members who have selected the children artworks for this book: Helga Piaget, Fiona Life, Maria Bologna, Victoria Cerrone, Lael Dewahl, Joyce Clear and Rosanne Sammis.

Water is Life:
Thoughts of Our Generation

Who we are

Passion Sea is a nonprofit Organization promoting on an international scale, the respect and preservation of our waters through education and creativity.

Helga Piaget, CEO, founded Passion Sea in 2014 and is the visionary behind the global effort to rehabilitate, restore and cherish the water of our planet. She is directing multi-level projects in conjunction with her daughter Fiona Life, a world-renowned artist, who is combining creative and visual elements as well as forging the connection between technology and nature.

Helga's son, Sandro Piaget, a professional golfer, is adds the sporting component through golf tournaments and gatherings in a variety of sports, raising the awareness and making tangible progress in arenas beyond the cultural and educational platforms, always in sync with the greater objective.

Passion Sea nominated two children Ambassadors to represent its mission and message around the world. Princesses Maria Carolina and Maria Chiara de Bourbon of Two-Sicilies are the "voices" speaking on behalf of children across the globe, collaborating with great enthusiasm for exposure in various media. Passion Sea focuses on youth during their formative years, as they become aware of the importance of protecting the Earth's waters. Children are in charge of the world of tomorrow and will shape its future. We help them understand, appreciate and love this precious gift of nature.

What we are doing

Passion Sea makes an impact all around the globe in many ways: through art, education, films and books. We allow children to understand that
"Water is Life: is not only what we need, is what we are".

The worldwide art contest, encompassing children up to twelve years of age, gives them space to express their feelings for this precious element of nature. This book delivers these special messages through art and poetry. We witness their love and fears. Simultaneously, we glean insights from scions of business, scientists, artists and public figures. This opens a conversation of our time through thoughts, innovative ideas and creativity.

We are mounting collaborations with schools and different educational entities. We are establishing programs, finalizing a book series for children, revealing compelling facts and experiments as part of their educational progression.

We are working with world class entertainment producers and composers on a Passion Sea signature theme song and musical production to spread the message across the globe.

Respecting water helps children respect our planet as well as each other, a humanitarian endeavor which can build exponentially!

Blue, the Mother of the Sea

Helga Piaget, Founder & CEO of Passion Sea

The Sea is the mother womb of the world. We are all part of this amazing natural element. Water fills our bodies and our majestic Blue Planet. The rivers, lakes, seas and oceans are vital for our survival on this planet. It is our priority to protect them.

In the Antiquity, water has been the symbol of purity. Our technology driven society has become indifferent to water and has taken this miracle of life for granted. In the last fifty years industries and farming only looked to increase productivity, neglecting all consequences for the environment. Plastic, first seen as a great invention, is becoming a life threatening enemy. It breaks my heart to see how water is so disrespectfully treated by humans and their unawareness to how dangerous their actions are for themselves and future generations. We need to have a holistic view and understand that there is a cycle of life for everything.

I have two children and want to transmit my passion to the next generations. Children are the adults of tomorrow who will be in charge of the decisions for the future of the world. Through PASSION SEA, I designed an international children's art contest inviting interpretations of their thoughts on the topic of water, through art and poetry. These tangible creations show us their love and fears. I hope this edition will awaken people of all ages within many environments to help them realize that their own lives are in danger. Education and drastic changes in our behavior could benefit the restoration of the balance of our Earth.

Let us all work together towards a healthier planet. Water is Life. it's our life!

Water for strength

Sandro Piaget, Sport and Sponsors Coordinator
& Treasurer of Passion Sea, Professional Golf Player

Life and Water go hand in hand, there is no life without it. Everything begins with water. As an athlete, I understand the crucial role water has on performance; a proper hydration is required to be successful. A healthy individual is composed of approximately 70% Water. That may vary a little based on the Fitness level and specific body composition, since muscles contain up to 75% of water.

The human body is very complex, capable of countless amazing tasks, while constantly repairing and regenerating itself. In sport, every competitor knows that recovery is the most important part of the training. When muscles are trained, they need rest and good nutrition to grow and recondition themselves even stronger. Water works various ways throughout the body's system from joint lubrication to delivering nutrients, flushing toxins. Regulating body temperature is another crucial role Water has on our overall physical constitution; it's the way we function. Think of the engine of your car - it needs to be kept at a certain temperature to perform its best. We are no different. Through exercise, our muscles create heat and our body temperature rises. To counter that, we start sweating through the evaporation process, as the temperature regulates itself. None of that is possible without water.

It is this endless cycle of Water supply that keeps us hydrated, regenerates and flows through all of us! We are all athletes in life, our body is our vehicle in this world. So let us all make an effort in preserving this great and vital resource!

Waterfall of Life

Fiona Life, Creative Director & Vice President of Passion Sea,
The Art of Transformation Artist

"Flow & Truth"
Mixed media Art by FIONA

Energy, as scientists know, is the source of everything. Atoms are an example of how energy works. The nucleus consists of protons and neutrons that compromise most of the weight of the atom, surrounded by electrons with a negative charge. Those are attracted electrically by the protons and surround them through an orbital dance. Reality is therefore a mix of the seen and the unseen.

Water is our most important resource. When our bodies are at optimal flow, we could say that internally they look like waterfalls. Waterfalls are one of the most amazing beauties of this world. They have the most negative ion content in nature; oxygen atoms charged with an extra electron. They help clear mold, virus, bacteria. They take the free radicals out of our body, helping with a better flow. They also increase our happiness level, sense of wellbeing, clarity, focus, as well as improve our sleep patterns. Waterfalls are an indicator of the health of our ecosystem. The combination of their beauty and natural composition supports us to be the best version of ourselves.

I create visual experiences called "The Art of Transformation". I use art as a way to crystallize beauty and the divine; to connect technology, science with spirituality and nature. My creations bring harmony into existence. By clearing our energetic spins from chaos into harmony we can break down the obstacles on a physical, mental and emotional level. Water is flow. When we become waterfalls, we embody the true meaning of the circle of life.

Flow & creativity

Fiona Life, Creative Director & Vice President of Passion Sea,
The Art of Transformation Artist

As an artist, I know firsthand the importance of igniting our imagination. The quest of diving deep inside oneself, in the ocean of the mind, is a rewarding process, chanelling and expressing inner throughts and visions. For children this is easy, as their minds are still pure - such a beautiful process to witness their desire to share unfiltered "opinions". Art is a universal tool and language. The use of symbols, colors, forms, composition and perspective is endless and brings forth a different narrative. No two visions are alike or expressed the same way. Those variations are similar to musical tones and describe the melody of our mind.

Imagination and creative thinking governs the right side of our brain. It is essential, especially for children during the evolutionary stages of their development, to be able to stimulate both sides of their brains. Our evolution is an ascension, building on experiences and assimilations. The more we are stimulated, the more we enrich ourselves, allowing our mind to blossom. Art is a way to express our vision of the world and relate our experience to others.

Applying a creative outlook to any perspective is a viable tool to achieve a holistic approach. Looking at a problem in a multidimensional way, one can easily pose the equation, identify the problems and devise solutions. Children are the future of tomorrow, thus our role is to inspire and guide them in their growth, while they remind us to keep our "inner child" alive.

"Water Ripple Blue"
Mixed media Art by FIONA

The Art of Passion

Lael Dewahl & Victoria Cerrone, LDVC Gallery

Every time I jump in the ocean, I feel like a kid! Like being in love, when we allow our bodies to be in the ocean, near it or around it, we **feel** something. This also happens to us when we are surrounded by fantastic, interesting and unique artwork! Water and art have the power to move our emotions and to create a genuine desire to explore. Depending on the temperature of the ocean or the type of art we are drawn to, we try to determine how the experience will unfold before rushing in full force. As time goes by in our lives, the meaning of the ocean evolves and art becomes part of who we are. Mind, body, and soul rejuvenation becomes possible with all the health and wellness benefits of the ocean and our ever changing relationship with art. Eventually, like someone you love deeply, the ocean becomes a part of everyday life, supporting every breath we take and supplying the very food we eat. If we love the ocean and it gives us so much, how can we **commit to protecting it?**

Commitment comes from a consistent and passionate investment in what matters most; through art we are able to express ourselves without fear of judgment, if we are free in our expression. The young people who shared their concern for the eco system were able to do so with freedom of expression. This generation is very much aware of what is at stake, this speaks to Maslow's hierarchy. We must have access to the basics of clean water if we are to continue as a species.

I have faith in human nature, especially in children and their ability to speak to what is their truth. We are committed to our children, to one another, and therefore we must be committed to the protection of the ocean. Art has the power to open our minds to what is possible and to remind and inspire us to care.

Water & Education

Rosanne Sammis, Teacher Benjamin School, Florida

One of the reasons I like to use water as an inspiration in my art class is because of its ability to energize and calm at the same time. Whether a wave or a colorful coral reef appears on the sea, I think children can see both. While water can have an action of a powerful natural force such as a wave, rain or even a hurricane, it can be serene and calm like a pond, tranquil sea or a fluffy cloud. Its colors are soothing and harmonious, something I strive to bring into my classroom environment and projects.

Children love water, the idea of the ocean is like a unique planet here on earth. Florida children live for the ocean..... they play, spend family time, fish, dive, and surf in it all year long. Children can express so many different feelings and experiences through water illustrations and artworks. Educating our youngest artists to be ambassadors of the oceans and of our planet reaches far into their lives beyond their elementary years in school.

As a teacher and Florida naturalized native of 35 years, I began my early time in Florida on the water. My Florida life was launched in 1985 studying wild dolphins on a boat in the Bahamas, I revel in sharing the experiences and passions that I cherish for the sea with my students. Be it fantasy worlds that children know through mermaids, books, and movies, or their own life experiences living so close to the sea, water is a precious element in their lives.

The Sea is our Family

Princess Maria Carolina & Princess Maria Chiara Bourbon Two-Sicilies,
Children Ambassadors of Passion Sea

To be ambassadors of Passion Sea is for us a great pride.

We were born bathed in the Mediterranean and have always been surrounded by the sea. The sea is for us a sort of third sister who follows us wherever we go. Why then not commit to protect her now that she is in danger?

We see the protection of the seas and oceans as a way of giving back to the world all the privileges we have had by birth. Somewhere being "Princesses" is for us like a motor, which propels us to do beautiful things!

We are lucky to have a dad who loves sailing and shared his passion with us. He introduced us to the beauty of the Mediterranean and was the first to let us know the sound of water striking on a boat, and we think that was a very nice way to make us aware of this. As we traveled with him, we realized the damage already done on the seas by finding along the coasts of southern Italy for example, waste that we had never seen before. Moreover, we live part of the year in Monaco, Prince Albert II, who witnessed the marriage of our parents, is also very sensitive to the well-being of the ecosystem and the oceans. So we can almost say that
caring for the sea and defending it is a bit like a family story!

We want to inspire the children to express themselves and to help make changes to

"The two mermaids represent my sister and myself who swim in a beautiful undersea world which one day will cease to exist."

EDUCATION CONTENT
The Culture of Water

Alessandro Leto, University Professor of Sustainable Development of Geopolitics for Natural Resources, Author of Scientific Publications and Award-Winning Documentary Films on the Environment, Served as Senior Advisor and Consultant for Italian Institutions and for UNIDO, where He Developed the Concept of *Sustainable and Responsible Development* in 2005

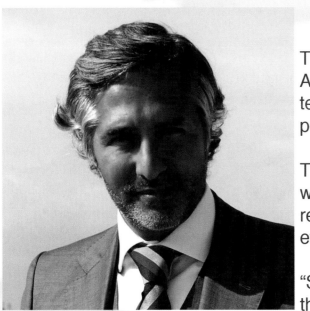

"Aman Iman", Water is Life.

This is an ancient aphorism quoted in Tamasheq, a language diffused in Western Sahara. And it's quite strange that all of us "Citizens of the World", especially those who live in territories rich in water, are forced today to learn the importance of Water from those populations who have lived a precarious, often traumatic, relationship with the "source of life".

The huge effort made by the UN in recent decades produced **extraordinary results**, especially with the affirmation of the Principle of Sustainable Development and the milestone represented by Agenda XXI and the related Rio Declaration. Also to be applauded are the efforts of scientists and scholars worldwide.

"Sustainable is the development that meets the needs of the present without compromising the ability of future generations to meet their own needs", Brüntland Commission (1987).

All that has been done until today, has not been enough. It is important to recall in our mind what Water really means for all living creatures on planet Earth. We must realize the importance of all forms of water. We can use Water as a sort of extraordinary lens through which to observe the complex interaction between humanity and nature in almost all its aspects, combining the factor of time, the territory and geography.

For a long time the balance between human beings and nature has been virtuous. Then, with the gradual affirmation of the industrial revolution, this same relation entered a more serious state of crisis. The invention of electricity and artificial light suddenly changed the rhythm of life in our modern societies, making the days artificially longer as well as intensifying the over-exploitation of natural resources. The increase in pollution of any kind, such as garbage and smog, became the consequence of the crazy competition against nature. Water, which together with air, is the only universal vector on Earth, became the major victim of this process. That historical period insured many positive conquests for humanity in different arenas, but at the same time we started to let our planet pay the price for those same conquests.

The situation became more critical when, in the mid 1900's, consumerism appeared with its ambiguous image of progress. Thus was created a sort of collective fever, that still burns today, to consume in a frantic way, almost all available natural resources of our planet. We consume, and consume, and consume again: day and night all over the Earth.

Today we do have to face the dramatic problem of water scarcity, including many places and territories where it was an unknown phenomenon just a few years ago, as in Europe. Despite warnings, we practice old habits, not taking into consideration how the waste of water is among the worst enemies of a balanced relationship between human beings and water. Almost 65% of water consumption is in agriculture, an economic activity that is often far beyond its traditional role to feed humanity. Fortunately, new technologies are helping in our engagement against the water waste. We must remember that every single drop counts !!!

We all feel the deep responsibility for our involvement and contribution, beginning with education. Education is the main pillar of the foundation to mount a better society tomorrow. To achieve this goal we must work to bridge the results and the progress made in all our fields of activity, to strengthen, root, diffuse and coherently practice the Culture of Water.

Hello! My name is Bubble.
I am 100% water.

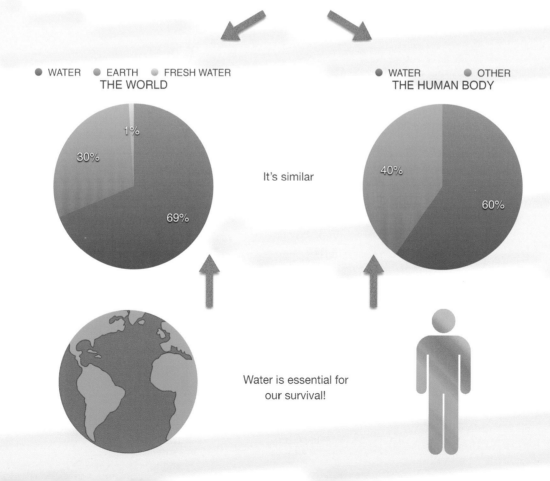

by Fiona Life

Did you know that 1 liter= 20'000 drops of water

DAILY ACTIONS	IN LITERS
WASHING OUR HANDS	10
CLEANING THE DISHES	40
WASHING THE CAR	200

FOOD PRODUCE (PER UNIT)	IN LITERS
SALAD (500 GR)	40
ORANGE	50
BANANA	66
APPLE	70
BROCOLI (500 GR)	105
BEEF (500 GR)	6000
CHICKEN (500 GR)	1800

FREQUENTLY USED ITEMS (PER UNIT)	IN LITERS
COMPUTER	40'000 - 150'000
TELEVISION	15'150- 246'000
CAR (~50000€)	4000000
TSHIRT	2150
JEAN	11000

Let me teach you some facts about water

Water is Life: Connection and Properties

Fiona Life, Creative Director & Vice President of Passion Sea,
The Art of Transformation Artist

Water is essential to our life. Approximately 90 % of our cells are composed of water. 50 trillion of them in our anatomy. If we lose 50% of the water in our body, we cannot survive. The same applies to animals and plants. Blood, other fluids and the very structure within any living creature or vegetation need water to reenergize. Water gives us all life.

Water is intelligent. It adapts to the shape of it's environment. Water constantly moves: from streams to rivers and oceans, in a microscopic torment to the swirling vapor of the clouds.

"Water is its mater and matrix, mother and medium. Water is the most extraordinary substance! Practically all its properties are anomalous, which enabled life to use it as building material for its machinery. Life is water dancing to the tune of solids" reflects Albert Szent-Gyorgyi, Nobel Prize winner (1972).

"The body of the earth is of the nature of a fish...because it draws water as its breath instead of air," said Leonardo da Vinci. He used to compare the human body's veins and arteries of blood with the flow of rivers. Da Vinci would often explain one system by referring to the other.

The water molecule is a simple structure of one oxygen atom bounding to two hydrogen atoms each at a 104.5° angle. The distance between O-H is 95.7 picometres. The electronegativity nature of the oxygen atom is important to understand water tetrahedron structure. Water molecule's polarity is also a factor in its level of dissolution of ionic compounds. This process, allows for example salt to be dissolved in oceans as well as any chemical reaction to sustain living organisms.

The Encyclopedia Britannica explains that "the molecules of water physical and chemical properties of the compound are extraordinarily complicated, and they are not typical of most substances found on Earth. For example, although the sight of ice cubes floating in a glass of ice water is commonplace, such behavior is unusual for chemical entities. For almost every other compound, the solid state is denser than the liquid state; thus, the solid would sink to the bottom of the liquid. The fact that ice floats on water is exceedingly important in the natural world, because the ice that forms on ponds and lakes in cold areas of the world acts as an insulating barrier that protects the aquatic life below. If ice were denser than liquid water, ice forming on a pond would sink, thereby exposing more water to the cold temperature. Thus, the pond would eventually freeze throughout, killing all the life-forms present."

The surface tension in water is due to its positive and negative charges as well as cohesive forces: water is attracted to water. Water is sticky. Molecules of water bound themselves together into drops.
Water's melting point is 0 °C (32 °F), and boiling point,100 °C (212 °F). Those can be seen as unusual temperature as not related to water molecules sizes or other analogous compounds.

Enzymes help break down food in our system so our body can easily digest and absorb them. The nature of water viscosity help accommodate this process as well as the dissolution and circulation of other substances like proteins.

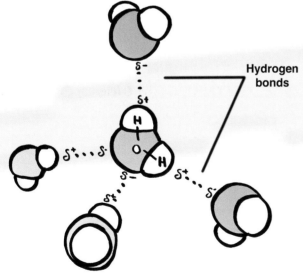

Chemical composition
of a water molecule bonding in water.
Illustration by FIONA

"Light and Water Nature Connection"
Photography by FIONA

Water is Life:
Cycle and Transformation

by Fiona Life

The hydrological cycle is the principle explaining water circulation on Earth. The balance on Earth depends on water's ongoing transformation from solid to liquid through exclusion zone and vapor.

"The sun, moving as it does, sets up processes of change and becoming and decay, and by its agency the finest and sweetest water is every day carried up and is dissolved into vapor and rises to the upper region, where it is condensed again by the cold and so returns to the earth. This, as we have said before, is the regular course of nature." Aristotle

"The "exclusion zone" (EZ), the unexpectedly large zone of water that forms next to many submersed materials, got its name because it excludes practically everything. The EZ contains a lot of charge, and its character differs from that of bulk water. Sometimes it is referred to as water's fourth phase. The atomic structure of ice closely resembles the atomic structure of the exclusion zone. This similarity is beyond coincidence: one transforms readily into the other" explains Dr Gerald Pollack, Author of "The Fourth Phase of Water: Beyond Solid, Liquid, and Vapor" (2013).

Photosynthesis is the process found in nature, of converting energy from the sun into food through the green pigments found in leaves called chlorophyll.The chemical equation is: $6CO_2$ (carbon dioxide) + $6H_2O$ (water)= $C_6H_{12}O_6$ (glucose) + $6O_2$ (oxygen)

Sunlight is white light but white light is actually the combination of all the colors of the rainbow. Therefore when sunlight hits water drops, they act like a prism, refracting and internally reflecting the colors. This phenomenon explains the creation of rainbows in the sky and on other surfaces.

The cycles of the moon influence the water on our planet. Every night we can see a different face of the moon due to its position in comparison to the Earth. Every day, our blue planet experiences tides; two high tides and two low tides, each lasting about six hours.Those are due to the moon gravity pull.

Water can be found anywhere, even in space! Meteors, comets and stars all have trace amounts of liquid in them.

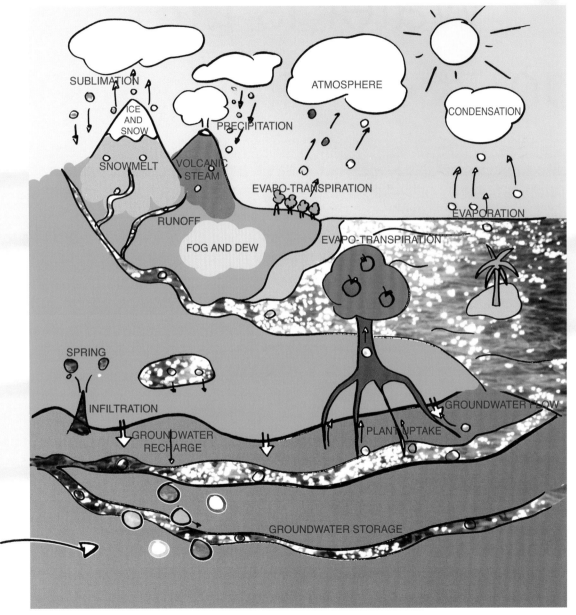

"Hydrologic cycle"
Illustration by FIONA

Water is Life:
Memory & Healing Properties
by Fiona Life

Photograph by Dr Masaru

This is me after you freeze me and show me Love and Gratitude!

Jacques Benveniste's work is the basis for the practice of homeopathy and it has serious ramifications by providing evidence for water's ability to store and share information.

"The crystals that are formed when water is shown positive words are simply beautiful. The response of water to love and gratitude is nothing less than grandeur. The positive words give spirit, which materializes it, to reveal life at its fullest" says Dr Masaru Emoto in his book "The hidden messages of water" (2004). "Based on the principles of vibration, the answer is very clear. All we need to do is emit the emotion that is opposite to the negative emotion. By combining two opposite waves, the negative emotion disappears." For example to clear anger, you need to vibrate kindness; to clear hate, you vibrate gratitude. "Our bodies consist of some 60 trillion cells, each carrying out its specialized responsibility while simultaneously harmonizing with other cells in a wonderful way to make us who we are. The organs, nerves, and cells of the body have their own unique frequency. The body is like a grand orchestra consisting of the harmonization of various sounds." Water is the great conductor.

Trees are the lungs of our planet. The similarities in between the way trees and lungs function and are structured is rather remarkable. They both have a central trunk or trachea, which is then divided into smaller branches to finish in leaves or alveoli, who are the center of the gas exchange. Oxygen is used to produce energy from carbon based compounds in our bodies cells while removing the carbon dioxide. The same process occurs in the respiratory tree system with one complementary step, known as photosynthesis. The dissolution of oxygen and carbon dioxide in both plants and humans is only possible through the unique qualities of water in every cells.

Flowing water, like rivers, oceans and waterfalls, is known to bring us a sense of wellbeing. Waterfalls are among nature's most amazing beauties of this world. They have the most negative ion content in nature: oxygen atoms charged with an extra electron. The negative ions help clear mold, virus and bacteria. They take the free radicals out of our body helping with a better function and flow. This helps increase our energy and happiness level, sense of wellbeing, clarity, focus as well improve our sleep patterns. Waterfalls are an indicator of the health of our ecosystem.

PranaView Australia espouses the following statistics: "Ion counts in fresh country air has a 2,000-4,000 negative ions per cubic centimeter. Large waterfall provide over 100,000 negative ions. Polluted air such as in large cities might have less than 100 ions."

Marian Diamond, a Professor of Neuroanatomy at the University of California, Berkeley, discovered that levels of negative ions are related to levels of serotonin in the brain. Serotonin controls mood regulations, pain perceptions and the sense of hunger and satiety. Negative ions suppress serotonin in the brain. For a healthier working and living environment, it is suggested to have living plants and moving water as well as natural fabrics which produce negative ions. Air conditioning and lack of ventilation remove negative ions from the air. It is therefore important to balance our environment. Knowing those facts can help you promote healthy changes in your day to day life.

"Rainbow Falls"
Photography by FIONA

Water is Life: Symbols and Rituals

by Fiona Life

The spiral and triple spiral date back to 10,000 BC. Some are found in the Megalithic Temples of Malta from the Neolithic Period. The Celtic have used the Triskelion as a symbol for motion, energy, cycle, the spiritual world, the present world and the celestial world. The connection to spirituality is often implied in the spiral reach for growth and to higher consciousness. Native Americans created spiraling labyrinths as a ritual passage to promote spiritual growth. The universe dances in a perpetual spiral movement. The double spiral is a symbol for eternity, balance, heaven and earth as well as the union of woman and man principle. It was often used in Egyptian and Celtic traditions. The Yin and Yang symbol reflects those meanings as well as the movement from non-manifestation to manifestation and vice versa. The Fibonacci sequence describes a spiral through the golden ratio. In plants and animals the spirals are called whorls. Look around you, and a newfound awareness will emerge perceiving the symbol in seashells, flowers, twisting trunks, animal horns, your fingerprints and so many other forms of flora, fauna and species.

The Native cultures praised the spirit of water which resides in water. They believed if the spirit of water was not in the water, that either bad things happened there or were going to happen. Water spirits and deities hold many names among different civilizations. Aztec mythology venerated Chalchiuhtlicue, goddess of all water forms. Celtic mythology had Gwragedd Annwn, female Welsh lake fairies and Acionna, water goddess. The Neck were Germanic mythology water spirits shapeshifter who appeared in human form, and the Undine was a female water elemental. Greek mythology had Naiads, nymphs who watched over water: Crinaeae in fountains, Limnades in freshwater lakes, Pegaeae in springs, Nereids in the sea and Sirens who were bird headed also in the sea near rocky islands. Their abundance of water gods is extensive and include Achelous, Amphitrite and Delphin. In Roman mythology, Camenae were the name of their nymphs. Japanese folklore had Kappa and Hyosube. In Slavic mythology, a Vodyanoy was a male spirit and a Berehynia, a goddess protecting the waterways. Animals associated with water such as whales, dragons and snakes were also worshipped around the world.

The Chinese and Japanese Kanji for water depiction was originally a river and became "areas of water" and three rippling lines. In the five elements it representing Yin and the female principle, water is soft and yielding. "Weak overcomes strong, soft overcomes hard" said Laozi in the Dao De Jing taoist texts. Taoist philosophy is "be still like a mountain and flow like a river." In China, water is the symbol of all life. Buddhism promotes the healthy living with your environment. In Shintoism, every worship starts by the act of water purification. The religion believes waterfalls to be sacred and the act of standing beneath one to be a purification act.

Many religions use water as a purification method from Christianity to Hinduism. From Genesis 1:2 to Revelations 22:17, the word water is written 722 times. In Christianity, baptism uses the concept of water as purification and liberation, the same is believed for Holy Water. The Koran states " We have created very living thing from water". Orthodox Jews practice the mikveh, a ritual of purification through immersion in water. In Islam, water is a gift from God; kudu, a washing ritual, is practiced after each of the five daily prayers. Baha'i Faith believes that water had a key role in the concept of creation. The respect they have for this element doesn't stop at this fact as they use it for a similitude of metaphors for spiritual truths. Zoroastrianism sees pure water as sacred and therefore to keep it that way. Aminism, traditional knowledge, is based on the caring for water as a sacred gift. In Hindusim, according to the Rig-Veda "… in the beginning everything was like the sea and without light." The River Ganges is considered the water of life for Hindus, as a rite for spiritual purification. It is considered to flow to Nirvana.

"Blue Effects"
Photography by FIONA

Water is Life: Protection & Pollution

by Fiona Life

LOVE ME + PROTECT ME

The yearly water consumption is provided by the United Nations (UN, UNESCO, and FAO):

9,200,000,000 million of liters of water have been consumed this year as of November 1st 2017.

50 - 67 oz (1.5 - 2 l) is the recommended amount of water needed per person per day.

300 gallon (1'135 l) of water per day is the average American family usage at home.

Changes in lifestyles and eating habits in recent years are requiring more water consumption per capita.

Almost 80% of diseases in so called "developing" countries are associated with water, causing some three million early deaths - for example, 5,000 children die every day from diarrhea, or one every 17 seconds.

Worldwide, agriculture accounts for 70% of all water consumption, compared to 20% for industry and 10% for domestic use. In industrialized nations, however, industries consume more than half of the water available for human use.

On average, 71% more energy to irrigate an acre field of corn than organic corn.

37% of freshwater withdrawals is used for irrigation.

41.5% of freshwater withdrawals is used for Thermoelectric Power.

Between 70% and 80% of the garbage found in the sea is made of plastic. 90% of the plastic waste comes from the shores, the large cities and currents. Plastic bags kill fish, birds and all marine life. The only way to decrease and cease this cycle would be to stop littering and using plastic bags and bottles.

50 billion plastic water bottles have been used by Americans in 2016 but only 23% of those bottles are recycled per year. This means that more then $1,000,000,000, one billion dollars of plastic is wasted each year.

WHAT I CAN DO TO HELP:
- I can avoid letting the water run when I brush my teeth, when I wash my hair or do the dishes
- I can be careful of what I throw down the sink and toilet
- I can take a shower instead of a bath
- I can avoid staying too long in the shower
- I can sort the waste and recycle
- I can consume less plastic (e.g. bags, bottles..)
- I can avoid having the light on unnecessarily
(When the light is on, it also uses water, as
51% of electricity is made with water!)
- I can avoid littering
- I can pick up the garbage I find in nature and in the water
- I can ask my parents, school, local restaurant.. to buy
organic products. Organic products don't use chemicals to grow,
don't poison the soil, nor the rivers and streams nearby.
They also need less water to grow crops.
- I can eat more fruits and vegetables
- I can use environmentally-safe household products to clean the house
- I can add more plants in the garden and to prevent contaminated
water from running into nearby water sources
- I can pray, send love to water and ask for the spirit of water to be
present in the water I drink and that surrounds me. I tell the water I drink, that
surrounds me and in my body: " I love you, I am sorry, please forgive me, thank you."

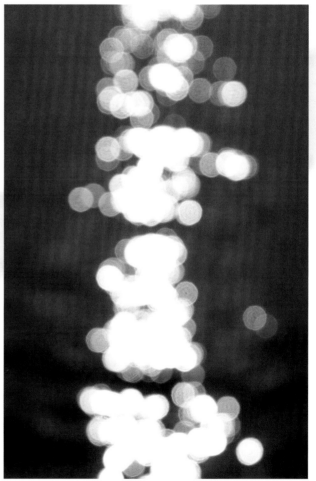

"Liquid Gold"
Photography by FIONA

Let's unite and join forces like drops of water to create a Passion Sea for change.

James Murphy, 4 years old, United States of America, Art Contest Prize Winner #1

The preservation of the seas is a vital cause for the living environment of future generations.

Hudson Kaplan, 10 years old, United States of America/ Japan

Art Contest Prize Winner #2

Andrea Bocelli

It is the crucial element of our planet, it is the primary matter of life, it is its origin and its maximum expression: water is the most relevant synonym for everything that is organic, to ourselves (that of water we are , In large part, compounds) and to what surrounds us.
In the body, as in the world, water is by its nature solvent: it dissolves and carries nutritional principles, just as it moves and nourishes and connects millions of people since the birth of human civilization. To break it down, to adulterate it, to subtract it, it means being enemies of life and triggering a degeneration that will not be able to turn back even to those who have caused it.
On such a delicate theme, more than so many - and often frightening - reflections and metaphors expressed by philosophers and poets, I think it is more useful (and more urgent) to evoke what Pope Francis

has said, with the simplicity and the concreteness that characterizes Its warnings: "The world has a serious social debt towards the poor who have no access to drinking water, because it means denying them the right to life rooted in their inalienable dignity."

Every human being can and must act, because water is really good for everyone. Through a project called "Water Truck", the Andrea Bocelli Foundation guarantees daily access to drinking water to more than 300,000 people in the slums of Cité Soleil, Haiti. Two tank trucks distribute more than 34 million gallons of water each year to the local community, significantly improving sanitation, limiting the transmission and spread of infections and reducing the risk of dehydration deaths in children and the elderly.

Tamana Khan, 7 years old, India, Art Contest Prize Winner #3

Michael Jordan

I grew up in a port city and later, spent the majority of my professional life in a city bordered by a great lake.

Improving and preserving the vitality of our oceans, seas, and waterways should be our ongoing priority.

Its about legacy and what we will pass on to our children and future generations. Let's work together, now, to leave them a priceless commodity: Clean water.

Princess Maria Carolina Bourbon Two-Sicilies, 12 years old, Italy, Children Ambassador

H.R.H. Charles of Bourbon Two-Sicilies,
Duke of Castro

Water is the essence of life. It flows through our veins, and regenerates our bodies. We all are children of the Oceans, as Mother Nature spoiled us with beautiful seas. For the sake of our children, and for the sake of Earth, we have to protect water for future generations.

The Sea

The sea makes me feel dreamy,
Boats passing by,
Turtles swimming in the dark Caspian Sea,
Plastic and engines killing sharks,
The waves of the rough sea makes me feel anxious,
Loneliness in the Red Sea,
Peace under the sea,
Sailing boats travelling over
the Mediterranean Sea,
And Lobsters being
killed for us to
eat.

Serenity in the Adriatic
Sea,
Anemones palpitating,
Jellyfish jiggling in the
warm sea.

Emerald fish caught by fishermen,
Carbon thrown in the sea, how awful!
The grey sea lions relaxing on the rocks,
And the sun shining on the smooth and
wonderful Sea!

Passion Sea 2014

Princess Maria Chiara Bourbon Two-Sicilies, 10 years old, Italy, Children Ambassador

H.R.H. Camilla of Bourbon Two-Sicilies,
Duchess of Castro

For the sake of our precious Earth,
For the sake of many awaiting Birth,
Let us protect the Treasure of Abysses
As if every drop of our blessed Ocean
Is a Pearl that deserves great Attention...

Ellie Donald, 4 years old, United States of America

Francesca von Habsburg

We are the only blue planet in the Universe! Let's keep it that way.

Sihle Makelene, 8 years old, South Africa

Princess Caroline Murat,
International Concert Pianist and Classical Music Festival Artistic Director

What will we leave as a memory for our descendants if we do not protect now, with all our strength, water and our natural environment.

At any time we preferred to live close to the water. What would become Venice, Bruges, Bangkok, Amsterdam, Suzhou irrigated by the genius of the man, if the water was running out? Roman pipelines, under ground of Nazca, Khmers irrigating the rice paddies, we need nourishing water. Without the oceans, wealth and knowledge, people would not have travelled so extensively through the centuries.The sailors sang it, source of the inspiration for poets, writers and painters, not to mention the fluidity of the impressionists: water is everywhere.

Where will our grandchildren go for a walk if already the gardens of Isfahan, "which smell like lemon and where the waters flow" are dry and don't reflect anymore the twenty columns that became forty in the mirror of the water. Perhaps they will go in those of Shiraz where "the water whispers and the birds are singing" or to Versailles with it's canals, fountains and jets of water?

If we do nothing, there might be only the tears left to irrigate the Aral Sea, whose disapppearance is one of the most important environmental catastrophes of the twentieth century. Desertification, depletion of soils, drying up of wells ahve been epidemic; Africa is devastated by the lack of water. Climate change brings its share of disasters, including typhoons, storms, floods, tsunamis, landslides in Asia, hurricanes, tornadoes, dry and burned land in the USA. Millions of climate refugees will migrate in the decades to come because of uncontrolled human activity.

This book from Passion Sea is essential because it brings us back to the essence of life, water! Let us gather to respect it, to love it on our planet in order to leave - without going to seek it on Mars-a better and more supportive world for our children.

Anastasia Seu, 10 years old, Monaco

Jack Nicklaus

Water is first and foremost a gift from God. It is one of the most important substances on earth. All plants and animals must have water to survive. If there were no water, there would be no life on earth.

Just writing those words makes me realize how blessed my family and I are to live by the ocean and to enjoy all that the Atlantic Ocean has to offer! I have a passion for boating, fishing, and golf. I simply enjoy looking out at one of God's greatest creations. Without water, my three passions in life would not be possible. Water is the support system for everything!

The ocean seems unending - and, yet our family has learned to appreciate not only the beauty of water - but the power of water.

We feel that water is symbolic of our relationship with God: carrying the image of renewal, promise, and hope.

Paolo Cavili, 11 years old, Italy

Ringo Starr & Barbara Bach

Peace & Love

We all need to wake up and realize how precious water is to us all - and take some responsibility for protecting it for us and generations to come. We are very much involved with WaterAid and totally believe in this work.

Zhou Dong, 9 years old, China

I learned from my environmental brother, Dr. Ian Player, many years ago that water is the world's most precious resource. Today it is more evident than ever that water conservation needs to be at the forefront of everyone's mind. It's imperative the people all around the globe come together to ensure future generations are not deprived of our main resource that is essential for life to survive and prosper.

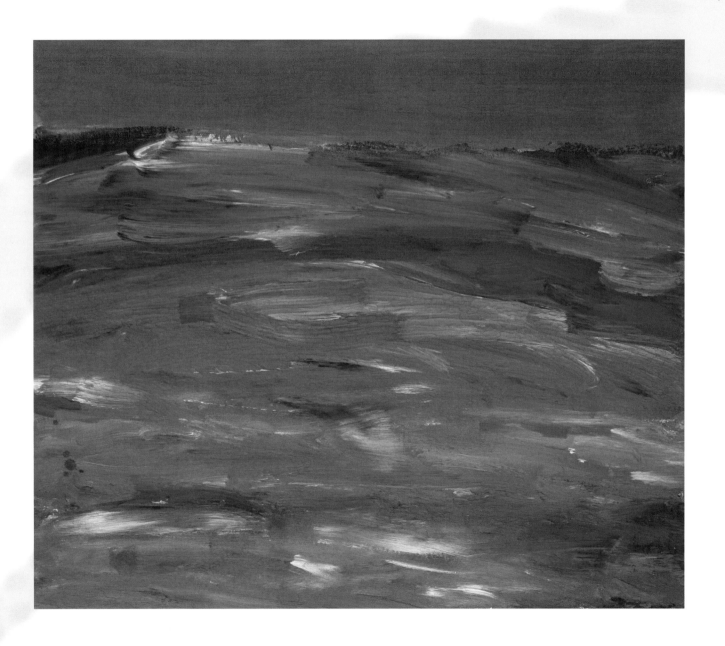

Sarah Darby, 10 years old, United States of America

European Commissioner for Environment, Maritime Affairs and Fisheries
Karmenu Vella, Our Ocean conference, October 6th 2017, Malta

If we are to have a green sustainable future, we have to look after our blue planet.

Sarah Darby, 10 years old, United States of America

John Englander, Oceanographer, Author of "High Tide On Main Street"

Water is the unique life-giving element of this planet, of all life. Water comes in varieties from the salty sea, to pure for drinking, and becomes a special salinity in our bodies. The point is that there are different aspects of water, just as there are different ways to view water. One can look at water from a scientific perspective, from an artistic perspective, and from a spiritual perspective. All are valid and important to connect us to this water planet and to conserve it.

This book is a wonderful lens through which to see it from the children's perspective, and to nurture their Passion for the Sea.

Conrad Luce, 10 years old, United States of America

Dr Gerald H. Pollack, PhD, Author of "The Fourth Phase of Water: Beyond Solid, Liquid and Vapor."

Our studies of water have revealed something new about the earth's most familiar substance, water. We found a fourth phase, beyond solid, liquid, and vapor. While our focus has been mainly scientific, the existence of the fourth phase implies something magical about water — a kind of underlying force that speaks to the long-standing issue of "living" water. Hence, I resonate strongly with Passion Sea's central theme and title of their wonderful book, "Water is Life."

Erika Seu, 10 years old, Monaco

Dr Masaru Emoto, Researcher and Author of
"Hidden Messages in Water" and "The True Power of Water"

We must pay respect to water, and feel love and gratitude, and receive vibrations with a positive attitude. Then, water changes, you change, and I change. Because both you and I are water.

Ashrick Philander, 11 years old, South Africa

Gaynor Rupert

The extensive use of plastic is a tragedy for our planet. We are grateful to Passion Sea for giving the children of "Imibala" in South Africa a positive approach for learning about the gradual destruction of our seas and marine life.

Through creative expression, children have an outlet to express their thoughts about these problems. Education is much more memorable, when making it fun and creative.

Hadley Nussbaum, 9 years old, United States of America

For a brand like PIAGET, born in the heart of nature, creativity can only arise at its contact, in the amazement of its perfect harmony. Water is a vital element in life and inexhaustible source of inspiration.

Batola Magwa, 11 years old, South Africa

Jean-Michel Cousteau, President,
Jean-Michel Cousteau's Ocean Futures

We need creative, optimistic, inspirational people who are using their talents to engage the future generation to use all means of creativity to care for our blue planet. Helga Piaget is one such talented artist and writer who is a great inspiration, sharing her love for the environment to inspire people to communicate the urgent need for action. She knows when people see and feel the beauty of the undersea world, they understand in a profound way, the need to take care of our water planet. Protect the Ocean and You Protect Yourself.

Liu Bao, 7 years old, China

Jean-Jacques Mantello, Director of "Wonders of the Sea 3D"

The 20th century has been a disaster for the environment, the 21th century has to be the environment century or humanity may not see the 22nd. "Water Is Life" this has never been so right, without healthy oceans, there is no life on earth....

Education and communication are the keystones of humanity, and solutions for a cleaner environment. Helga, your contribution and your involvement in education is important and it gives me hope for future generations.

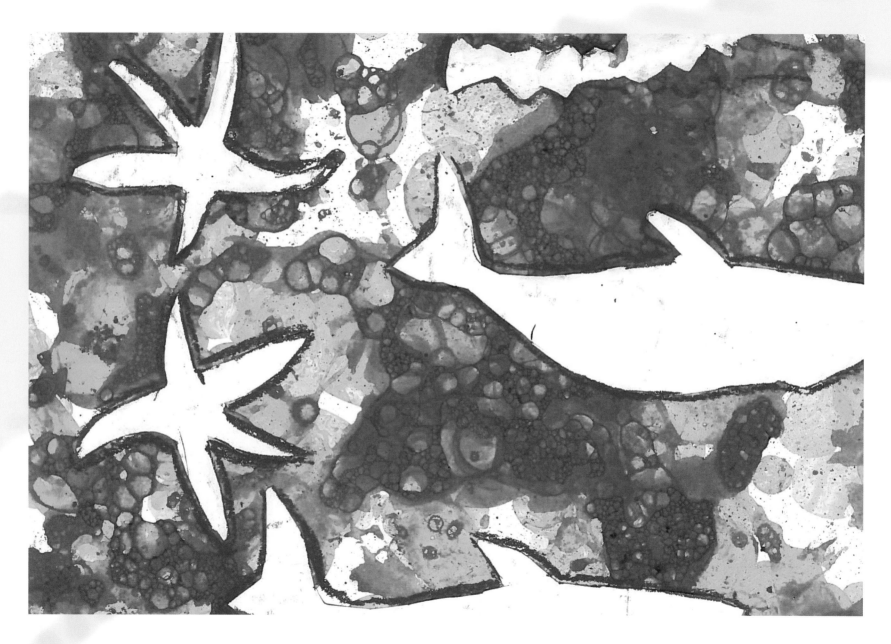

Jean Donval, 9 years old, Monaco

While we are searching for water and life in the universe, we are neglecting what is so precious down here on our blue planet. What allows us to be here. What provides the chemistry we need to exist: The Oceans.

Fulbano Ali, 8 years old, India

Ahmad Rashad, College Hall of Fame, NFL all pro,
Emmy Award Winning Broadcaster,
Executive Producer of NBA & Honorary Doctorate

*Water! Can't live without it!!
It is Life's Wonderful Elixir!
Beautiful, Abundant and...
Available to all??*

Katja Stranzinger, 8 years old, Germany

Marc Pajot, Olympic Medalist,
5 Time Winner of The "Route du Rhum", a Transatlantic Solo Race,
Knight of Maritime Merit, Officer in The National Order of Merit

From my youngest age I was lucky enough to discover the dinghy with my brother Yves in the bay of La Baule on the Atlantic coast.
We used to sail like any other sport for pure leisure. This game became fast my passion.
In our beginnings the competition attracted me as much as the sea. It became my work!

Always to improve, to profess, to discover the winds of the waves, a subtle and indomitable world. I've learned that we always learn and that the basic rule, when you go on the water, is that it is the sea and the wind that decide. This rule imposed by the Oceans has become my rule of life: Respect! Respect for others and respect for the elements.

The sea has taught me, working alone or as a team, that you never have acquired to suffer in silence, that you never are allowed to let go, that you have to assume....
Being with the sea, it is to love life and to think positive .

But we navigators, we made the observation with the scientists , that the man is a destroyer. Pollution, global warming are very real. Together with and for the oceans we have to become warriors to protect the waters of our planet. We have to give meaning to our life, to the gifts of nature for the sake of our children!

Joshua Mayer, 7 years old, Germany

Emmanuel Coindre, Professional Athlete,
World Record Holder in Ocean Rowing

The Ocean is a landscape where the imaginary and the sacred meet. It is a place of trial and initiation, demand and pleasure in which you surrender to have conversations, as meditating, sailing alone is to learn to remain bound to the divine world.

The attraction of the great blue is representative of our existence and essence. Our life is intimately linked to the oceans and the marine ecosystem carries as much beauty as fragility. Water is the most precious resource so let us act with full awareness.

Deepa, 12 years old, India

Álvaro de Marichalar y Sáenz de Tejada
Spanish Sea Explorer, Sailor Holding 12 World Navigation Records,
Academic Member of the Royal Academy of the Sea

Ocean conservation is key for our survival. The Blue Planet we live in is just a tiny drop of water traveling at very high speeds along the endless Universe... God created it and created us. We must act responsibly enough not to destroy our fragile **Ocean Planet***.*

Amy Li Fang, 9 years old, China

The Honorable Beverly White Yeager, Philanthropist & Patron of the Arts,
Former Director, Division of Cultural Affairs, State of Florida,
Institute of Museum Services, Board Member appointed by President Ronald Reagan

I have always been inspired by water and the sense of tranquility it imbues in my spirit. The sea takes my imagination on a ocean voyage to infinity of the mind. Water IS Life, our very essence within, purity of existence.

the Looking
of the glamorous
orange sun!

the beautiful
dolphin jumping
out of the sea
to say
hello

the feeling
of waves crashing
on the
magnificent
tan sand

under the sea
fish, dolphin, starfish...
the blue waters full
of treasure and life

Lauren Bohbot, 11 years old, Monaco

Katherine Balpataky, Editor, Water Canada

Without water, we would not have this magnificent planet Earth. Every time that I dip my toe into a stream or wade into a Great Lake, I remind myself that we are blessed to have fresh water.

ഗ THE SEA ഗ

About 70% of the world is covered with water.

97% of the water on earth is salt water.

Salt water is full with salt and minerals, because of that nobody can drink that water.

2% of the water is **glacier ice**
This ice is fresh (and could be melted), however, it is too far from where we live to be useful.

Less than 1% of all the water on earth that is **fresh water** that we can use.
We use that small amount of water for washing and drinking.

Everything is made out of **atoms.**
Atoms are the smallest component of molecules.
Atoms join together and form **molecules.**
A water molecule has only **three** atoms:
2 H (hydrogen) and 1 O (oxygen)
That's why water is sometimes called H_2O.
A **single** drop of water contains billions of tiny water molecules.

Sarah Darby, 10 years old, United States of America

Traver Kennedy, Chairman and CEO, Joi Scientific

Water is a magical substance. Our oceans contain a tremendous amount of energy and hold the great potential to meet the world's need for abundant, clean energy. By observing nature with open eyes and an open heart, Joi Scientific is developing innovative technologies to unleash hydrogen from seawater to power our planet. We call it Hydrogen 2.0.

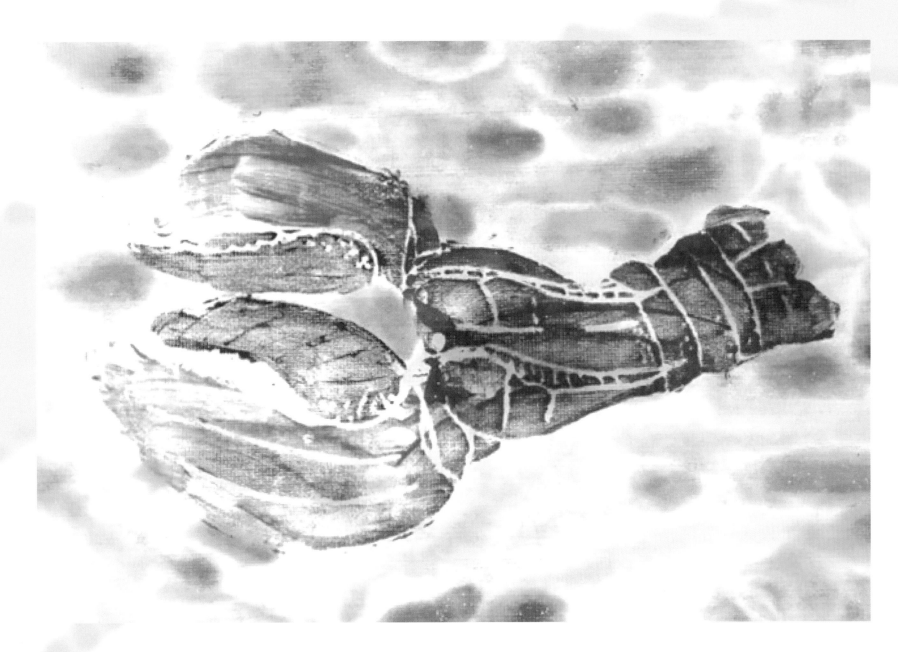

Alex Smith, 10 years old, United States of America

Professor Denis Allemand, Physiologist,
Scientific Director of the Scientific Center of Monaco

Greek mythology placed Ocean and Thethys, his sister and wife, as the parents of all beings. Today's science confirms the key role of the Ocean not only in the evolution of life, but in its maintenance during geological and present time.

If the Oceans have allowed life to appear, they have also been the origin of the formation of dioxygen (O_2). Our Ocean also limits the greenhouse effect caused by the production of carbon dioxide (CO_2).

60% of the world's population lives near the oceans, six of the eight cities with more than 10 million habitants are coastal. The Oceans are both a source of leisure (coastal tourism accounts for 60% of total tourism) and a source of food (fishing and aquaculture provide sustenance for about 12% of the world's population), while providing jobs (1 in 6 jobs in the USA is related to the Oceans).

But men in exchange for these services pollute the oceans, their CO_2 emissions heat the waters, causing the disappearance of ten square kilometers or more of coral reefs around the world, and acidify them. We urgently need to recognize that Oceans are fundamental to our own survival and to notify without delay, that it is vital for us and our future generations, to protect them NOW.

Akanksha, 8 years old, India

Patrick Rampal, President of the Scientific Center of Monaco

The Ocean covers more than 70% of the globe's surface, regulates the Earth's climate and houses a large part of the still unexplored biosphere. Ocean health is a crucial issue for the global climate, but also for the survival of living organisms including the human species. However the ocean is severely threatened by environmental changes, so it is urgent that we all participate in the preservation of "our" Ocean.

Lazola Magwa, 10 years old, South Africa

Dr. Michael Heithaus, Dean, College of Arts, Sciences & Education Professor, Department of Biological Sciences, Florida International University

Oceans are so vast, it's easy to forget how surprisingly fragile they actually are. We need to do more to learn about them and protect them. We must provide inspiring education to ensure there are future generations of marine scientists, ocean enthusiasts and decision-makers willing to do what is needed to protect and restore our oceans. We must never forget that to have a healthy planet, we must have healthy oceans.

Amy Benson, 11 years old, Monaco

Dr. Jeremy J. Kiszka, Research scientist,
Florida International University, Miami

As a marine ecologist and conservation biologist, I study the lives of whales, dolphins, sharks and sea turtles. These creatures are the ultimate ambassadors of our oceans. However, these species and their habitats are in danger. They face multiple threats, including ocean pollution, habitat degradation, incidental captures in fishing nets and lines, as well as climate change and ocean acidification. Preserving their habitat, including aquatic habitat quality, will be crucial for the survival of these species. The conservation of these large animals is therefore critical to maintain the health of marine ecosystems. Around the world, people also rely on these animals and their habitats for their livelihoods. They create amazing opportunities for ecotourism and the non-consumptive use of these animals. However, we will also have to generate new ideas to better consume and use our resources. This is where science meets conservation and people well being. Even though marine ecosystems experience major issues at the global scale, we need to remember that oceans feed our planet and play a critical role in the balance of our climate. They also feed our inspiration, our passion, and our enthusiasm to make this planet a better place for us and for generations to come. The more our planet faces challenges, the more people get involved and want to contribute to ocean conservation and water preservation. This book is an outstanding example...

Lucy Tosta Veiga, 10 years old, Portugal

Brett Jenks, President & CEO of Rare

No matter who we are or where we live, we all depend on a reliable supply of clean, fresh water. Unfortunately, droughts, pollution and man-made behaviors threaten this supply. But, there is hope. While people are at the root of many water conservation challenges, we also hold the solutions. By changing our behaviors and inspiring support for water conservation, everyone, especially young people, can play a meaningful role in protecting our oceans, lakes and rivers for future generations.

Wang Wei, 12 years old, China

Jean-Sébastien and Claudia Robine, President & Founder Club Des Leaders

Water is a precious substance that supports the immense diversity of life on our Mother Earth. We need a healthy planet to provide the clean water we need for our daily life.

It helps renew us culturally and physically.

As responsable and respectful citizen the "Club des Leaders" is proud and honored to support this philanthropic, generous and noble cause of our member Helga Piaget through her project PASSION SEA.

Zhang Hu, 10 years old, China

Joyce Clear, Founder, Ports of Cause; CEO, Clear Group International

My reverence of the oceans was engrained in me since I was a child and I have always known I wanted to give something back through my work since then. I come to ocean advocacy from a solution-oriented position and founded Ports of Cause, a 501(C)(3) non-profit, to promote, inspire, and accelerate sustainable, progressive solutions and practices across all sectors, while strengthening the inextricable link between ocean health and the wellbeing of all life. If we can provide people with easy, beautiful, sustainable choices to integrate into their everyday lives, the ocean will inevitably be the beneficiary. Let's get to the root of Ocean Wellness through a preventative approach.

Muskan, 9 years old, India

Jeremy P. Feakins, Chairman of the Board,
Ocean Thermal Energy Corporation

For billions of people living in parched, arid countries, the stark reality of a warming planet has meant increasingly unpredictable water supplies. Renewable energy like Ocean Thermal Energy Conversion (OTEC) uses the temperature differential of the ocean to power water desalination systems. OTEC can deliver millions of gallons of fresh water per day in a truly sustainable manner. OTEC lowers the cost of producing fresh water from the sea and provides environmental protections for marine life, too.

Yogita, 10 years old, India

Claude Béglé, National Adviser / Federal Assembly (Switzerland)
President, SymbioSwiss

Water is the blood of the world. When it flows in ideal fluid motion and quantity, civilizations flourish. Unfortunately the abuse of human activity tends to asphyxiate the flow. Therefore the potential for conflict swells rapidly.

If there were doctors in charge of the health of the world, no doubt they would prioritize the state and distribution of water in the various parts of the body of their patient, directly affecting not only the health but also wellbeing of the planet.

For many of us, water is something that we take for granted, far from rare. But this is an optical illusion. In many parts of the world, water is a precious treasure. It is up to us to maximize its essential worth. Let us call together "Water Assizes" and together define the best judgements for its use. We need to value Water as it deserves to be cherished and take advantage of new technologies to develop new applications.

Let's make water a source of prosperity, peace and hope!

Filippo Ferrogina, 10 years old, Italy

Guy Laliberté, Founder, Cirque du Soleil – President, One Drop

I contemplated Planet Earth and its precious resources from above, in all its strength and fragility, and it is a masterpiece.

Our planet, our water is a gift that inspires profound respect and instills a sense of wonder: With that comes a responsibility, that we all share. We need to realize that every one of us can and must cherish and protect this heritage.

As a creative entrepreneur, a businessman, but firstly, as a human being, I am reminded daily that water is life. One Drop was my way of expressing my gratitude, adding a drop to the collective efforts towards a world where the word thirst no longer has a meaning.

Basya Serova, 10 years old, Russia

Our beautiful oceans, lakes, rivers and shorelines of all kinds are frequently littered with garbage. Many wildlife call these shorelines home and it's up to us to help protect them. Change starts with action and we can all make a difference by making small everyday changes to reduce the amount of litter in our waterways. You can say no to single-use plastics like straws and water bottles and reuse materials instead of buying new products. Since 1994, Canadians have removed more than 1.2 million kg of shoreline litter, keeping countless species of wildlife safe from harm as well as protecting our beautiful aquatic ecosystems. Talk to your friends about how they can help too. It's important for all of us to do what we can to lend a hand.

Sapna, 12 years old, India

Bernadette Conant, CEO, Canadian Water Network

Children are naturally curious about science and the natural world. We must nurture this curiosity, as they will be the next generation of water consumers and decision makers. For the past two decades, I've encouraged young people from across Canada to look at how science can help us answer some really tough questions instead of 'telling us what to do.' What choices are possible? What are the implications for each choice? For me, that's what's really exciting about science – getting to the 'so what' moments that illuminate the possibilities and help us be confident about moving the world forward.

Blake Barham, 5 years old, France

Alex Mifflin, The Water Brothers, SK FILMS

From the tiniest insect, to your own body, and even the largest animal that has ever lived, the Blue Whale, we are all made of water. How we care for water today has long lasting implications for the health of our families, friends and every living thing on Earth, both today and for generations to come. When you protect water, you are protecting all life on this beautiful planet.

Sofia Gilardi, 7 years old, Monaco

Herme de Wyman Miro, Founder & President,
The International Society of Palm Beach

I believe with all my heart that water is life for humankind and animals. I want to stress the importance of keeping our oceans, lakes and all other waters pure and uncontaminated. We must preserve this precious element. Otherwise we will be faced with sickness and death.

Clara Fillery, 9 years old, Monaco

Ana Ros, Word Chef of 2017

I am happy to live in one of the most stunning corners of the world.. Never ending green forests and emeralds crystal clear waters make the Soča valley really a magical place.

Our rivers are home to a true Queen fish-the magical marble trout. Let' s call her Vera. Vera is a wild animal, very fast, intelligent and difficult to catch. I can spot her sometimes during my long walks along the river. For her life she needs the cleanest possible cold waters and a lot of oxygen.

But Vera was almost gone. A man was convinced he was wiser then the nature. He did not understand that Vera needs her own space where she can live, hide and catch. He wanted more fish in the river and he took a wrong decision. A man populated the waters with a rainbow trout. Vera was a better fighter, wilder and more beautiful but the genes of her new roommate were stronger. In the following 50 years Vera disappeared from the Soča river. She was almost gone.

A wise man came. He wanted Vera back. He was searching for her everywhere. One sunny warm day he finally found her. She was old like the Mother Earth and imagine how she survived all the way from the ice era. The greedy man could not harm her because she was hiding between two waterfalls and asked the rainbow trout to steer her home. The wise man was very clever, he did not want to rush. With patience and intelligence he convinced her to go back. Today the Soča river is a home to a lot of Vera(s).

In slovenian language Vera means hope.

I can only hope that my children will read this story to their children. And you can read this story to your closest friends, brothers and sisters.

We really don't want Vera to leave us again.

San Francesco, 6 years old, Italy

Veronica Ferres, Actress

Nature plays a big role for me.
In my childhood we grew up very naturally, as it was
then common in the countryside.
Already at that time I felt a great longing for the Sea.
My work allows me to travel to different places,
the Ocean is my favorite.
Water is the origin of life and not only that, the human
body is composed of 75% of it.
Water is life. Therefore we must do everything to protect
our Blue Planet and preserve the purity of the water.
Only then we will have a future.

Francesca Frizzi, 9 years old, Italy

Harold Riley, Artist, Royalty Portrait Painter

Rain falling from the sky like strings of pearls down my window pane...

The water droplets of our atmosphere are bringing down to the earth all the pollution in the air. Acid rain is effecting human health and most living species on the planet. We need to learn how to preserve the water of our Blue Planet so it can stay healthy today and for the future.

HE SAW THE SEA

From the sea, From the sea
All things came from the sea
He saw the sea, He saw the sea
He wanted all, When He saw the sea
To those that see, To those that
See..
All has come to those that see!

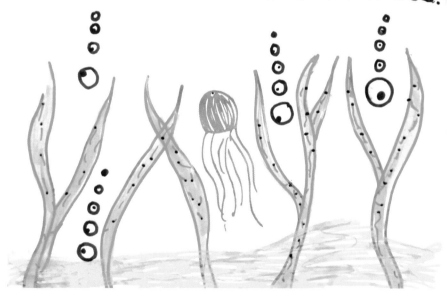

Maria Mazanova , 9 years old, Monaco

Tony Browne, Marina Director, Porto Montenegro

Porto Montenegro recognizes that responsible tourism is as much about giving to the local community as it is about protecting the natural environment. As a progressive world leading Superyacht Marina, Porto Montenegro has teamed up with the Seabin Project as a pilot partner. Maintaining a clean and rubbish free marine environment has always been an important focus for Porto Montenegro. Partnering with Seabin Project allows us to not only improve our waterborne refuse collection methods, but to also become part of a bigger environmental initiative by way of educating the next generation in the importance of environmental awareness, and the recycling / upcycling of existing refuse.

Cristina Marchesi Schlereth, 11 years old, Monaco

Isabelle Bonnal, Director of National Education,
Youth and Sports of the Principality of Monaco

It is our duty to transmit to younger generations a sense of respect for what is essential to us. In this responsible approach, guaranteeing to the greatest number to have access to water, which is a means of life, is a major challenge for the decades to come.

Today it is more then ever, for all mankind, an invaluable resource without which no future is possible. May the youth of this world be the guarantor of a harmonious world respectful of this source of life.

j'abore
la mer

Ines Briere, 8 years old, Monaco

Mrs Angela Godfrey, Head of Admissions and Public Relations,
The International School of Monaco

The future of our oceans, and indeed our planet, rests with the young conservationists whose imaginative paintings reflect their love of the sea and an early awareness of Earth's fragility. Only through education can we hope to reverse the damage we have already done.

We all have a responsibility to educate our young people on how their future lives, and the survival of this beautiful earth, rests with them. As these beautiful paintings show it is never too early to become aware of our very life source – the sea.

The outstanding quality and imagination of these paintings gives us hope for the future: that our young people will all become passionate about conservation and protecting our most vital resource – the sea.

Special thanks to our supporters

PIAGET

HAUTE JOAILLERIE
piaget.com

Making progress together by standing together

When you have the acceptance and support of an entire community behind you, the future is yours to make.

U.S. Bank Private Wealth Management is proud to support Passion Sea 501(c)(3).

Darlene A. Dzuba
Vice President, Senior Trust Officer
561.653.3357
darlene.dzuba@usbank.com

Rob Ford
Vice President, Private Wealth Advisor
561.653.3344
rob.ford@usbank.com

privatewealth.usbank.com

Fiona Life

"The Art of Transformation"

www.fionalife.com

Portion of Net Proceeds from the "Water drops" series will go to Passion Sea

Di Pasquale Guthmann

ROMA

www.dipasqualeguthmann.com

Let's join forces...

Lexye Aversa, Editor of Passion Sea, International Travel Expert, featured as "Best Global Event Planner" on FOX TV's Best of South Florida, President Professional Touch International, Producer/Media Host of LEX TRAVEL

Collaborating with Helga Piaget and FIONA was an honor. It has been a gift to be immersed in this endeavor; I could have never imagined such involvement would result in oceans of knowledge. Now I perceive Water with new eyes and reverence, trusting this will be your impression as well. We can all gain an elevated respect for our planet and affirmation of Life.

Flowers, Trees, Plants and Species give Birth Anew.... through Generations Grow, but
The Water We Have is The Water We Have, to Cherish and Replenish Life as We Know....

We are blessed to know that as humans, it IS within our power to protect, revitalize and preserve Water in its many forms. It is our "divine" responsibility to do so. Everyone who embraces "Passion Sea" will hopefully be galvanized from the messages of inspiration. Together, let us join that wave propelling us into a spiral surge of positive energy to restore Water!

PASSION SEA

info@passionsea.com

www.passionsea.com

Passion
Sea

"Let's join forces and unite
like drops of water
to create a Passion Sea for Change"